Special Stories Publishing
www.specialstories.net

Acknowledgements

Many thanks to Kieran, my father Michael, my brother George and my extended family and friends. Special thanks too to my uncle Liam Gaynor, Liz O'Donoghue, Eva Byrne and the Louth County Enterprise Board for their endless encouragement, support and invaluable advice.

Special thanks to Frances Guiney from the Asthma Society of Ireland and to Bettina Korn Respiratory Clinical Nurse Specialist, St. James's Hospital, Dublin for all their help and advice.

Special thanks also to Dr. Gerard Molloy Ph.D C.Psychol. whose time and effort with this project was so greatly appreciated.

About the Illustrator

Natalie Price is a multi-disciplinary artist. Her extraordinary commitment to creative work led her to complete eight years in third level education, developing professional skills in graphic design, illustration and model making. Natalie has a passion for the craft of physical model making. She pays great attention to detail when creating her charming illustration models. Natalie spends hours delving through all sorts of interesting materials, from piles of shiny fabric and boxes of watch and clock parts, to drawers of unusual beads and jewels, or whatever she finds at the bottom of her treasure chest. As well as building models from raw materials such as modelling clay, wood, and wire, Natalie's creative spirit often rescues items from the scrap heap; the lid of an old make-up bottle is rejuvenated as a miniature coal bucket or a pen holder, and an old watch casing is transformed into a picture frame.

Photography by Aaron O'Reilly. Website **www.aaronoreilly.com**

Kate Gaynor

for my dad

The Special Stories Series
The Winner

by **KATE GAYNOR**
Model Illustrations by **NATALIE PRICE**
Photography by **AARON O'REILLY**

Published in 2008 by

SPECIAL STORIES PUBLISHING

Member of CLÉ – The Irish Book Publishers Association

ISBN 978-0-9555787-3-1

A catalogue record for this book is available from the British Library

Printed by
BELVEDERE PRINT LTD. DUBLIN, IRELAND

Hi! my name is **Michael**. I am five years old.

Last year when I was four, I joined a brand new school and soon after that I found out that I had asthma.

Having asthma doesn't mean you are any different to your friends. It just means that sometimes air can't move in and out of your lungs the way that it should and that sometimes you might find it hard to breathe.

3

My doctor, Doctor Dan, knows all about asthma. He helped me to learn about the type of things that can cause an asthma attack.

Smokey air or even cold weather can sometimes make breathing hard for me. The most important thing to remember is to listen and follow carefully what your doctor or your mum and dad say when you are learning to use your inhaler.

Doctor Dan says that most boys and girls with asthma will sometimes need to use an inhaler. An inhaler is filled with special medicine that you inhale into your lungs to help them feel better.

Inhalers come in all shapes, sizes and colours and are used at different times for different reasons. Sometimes you might need to use a spacer with your inhaler. A spacer can make it easier for you to inhale the medicine in your inhaler.

ound out that I had asthma, I didn't like taking my
I thought it tasted kind of strange and I didn't like
to use it.

But not long after I started school, something happened that made me change my mind about my inhaler and my asthma forever!

That year in school my teacher was planning a very exciting day called a 'sport's day' for all the boys and girls. At the sports day children could take part in all sorts of games and races to win really great prizes.

When I told my mum about the sports day she promised that if I took my inhaler when Doctor Dan said I should, that I could go along with all of my friends.

But I wasn't a very good boy and I didn't listen to Doctor Dan or take my inhaler at all.

At school, everyone was practising their events for the big sports day. The other boys and girls with asthma were all practising too.

A couple of days before the big sports day, I told my mum that I was sorry for not taking my inhaler when she had asked me to.

I promised her that from that day on I would try my very best
to always follow what Doctor Dan and my mum or dad asked
me to do for my asthma.

When the sport's day finally arrived my mum came to school
with me. The school field was full of boys and girls all getting
ready for the big sport's day.

My mum said that she was very proud of me for learning how to take my inhaler and for listening to Doctor Dan. "That makes you a winner even if you don't win a prize today!" she said.

When the time came for our class race we all lined up at the start line ready to run the very best that we could. "Go!" shouted the teacher and we all started running towards the finish line.

Before I knew it, I had crossed the white finish line and won the class race! When the teacher handed me my prize and a golden trophy with my name on it, I knew that I really was a winner!

If you are a boy or girl with asthma learning to use an inhaler, remember you could be a winner too some day just like me! So do you have a special story like mine? Why don't you tell me all about it on your Special Story Page?

Your Special Story Page

Kate Gaynor

Notes for Grown Ups on Asthma

Asthma is a condition that affects the airways the tubes that carry air in and out of the lungs. When an asthma sufferer is exposed to something that irritates their airways, such as dust, their airways become narrower, making it difficult to breathe.

There are two main groups of medication used to treat asthma called Preventers and Relievers. The Preventers need to be taken on a regular basis by all asthma sufferers to prevent breathlessness and reduce the risk of a full blown asthma attack. Although medication for treatment of asthma comes in a variety of forms, the inhaler is the most popular and widely used as it delivers treatment directly to the place where it is required.

How to use this book:

By reading this story with your child, he/she can see the positive experiece of a fellow asthma sufferer. It firstly reassures them that they are not the only child dealing with Asthma and that many other children just like them are going through the same things that they are. It is important that they understand the importance of taking their inhaler regularly and that by doing so, they can take part in the same activities as all of their classmates and friends. The story introduces the idea that taking an inhaler on a daily basis can lead to instant and positive results.

For information on asthma please contact your local asthma association.

Kate Gaynor

Other books from Special Stories Publishing

A FAMILY FOR SAMMY: The purpose of this book is to help explain the process of foster care to young children aged 2-6 years.

JOE'S SPECIAL STORY: The idea of this story is to help explain inter-country adoption to young children aged 2-6 years.

FIRST PLACE: This book was written to help children aged 2-6 years to understand and accept the effects of cleft palate, cleft lip or any speech impediment in their lives and most importantly, how best to overcome them.

THE LOST PUPPY: This book has been designed to help children with limited mobility aged 2-6 years to see the positive aspects that using a wheelchair can bring to their lives.

THE BRAVEST GIRL IN SCHOOL: The objective of this story is to help children with diabetes aged 2-6 years to appreciate the importance of taking their insulin injections and being aware of what they eat.

THE FAMOUS HAT: The goal of this book is to help children aged 2-6 years with leukaemia (or other forms of cancer) to prepare for treatment, namely chemotherapy, and a stay in hospital.

To read more about the special stories collection, visit the Special Stories website at:
www.specialstories.net